The G

777 Rea

B. Craig Jones

"Reflect upon your present blessings, of which every man has plenty;
not on your past misfortunes, of which all men have some."

- Charles Dickens

Doozybird
Publishing

The Gratitude List
777 Reasons to be Grateful

Copyright © 2021 B. Craig Jones

ISBN 978-1-7331853-6-3 (Paperback)
ISBN 978-1-7331853-7-0 (Hardback)

Library of Congress Control Number: 2021907937

Published by:

Doozybird Publishing
PO Box 6991
Sherwood, AR 72124

Doozybird.com
craig@doozybird.com

The Gratitude List

INTRODUCTION

There are so many things to be grateful for regardless of all the negativity in the world. It's easy to get so busy that we don't notice the blessings around us or take the time to be grateful. It is difficult to see the "miraculous in the common," as Emerson said. Sometimes it just takes a change of focus - a conscious effort to notice the good and be grateful for it.

Studies have shown that counting our blessings, reflecting on them, and expressing gratitude for them, is good for us - mentally, emotionally, and physically. But where do we start? This book can help with that. Of the thousands of good things we experience in our lifetime, I list 777 of the more memorable or common reasons to be grateful. These are ones that many can relate to, and this list can help you think of reasons that you may not otherwise. There are even a handful of things here that may bring back a happy, forgotten memory. When these things come to mind, or you think of some on your own, reflect on them and be thankful.

There is much here to enjoy. This book is like an All-You-Can-Eat Food Buffet (Reason # 105) - take what you like and ignore the rest. Nothing here is embarrassing or shocking that you wouldn't want a young child to read or hear (unless it's #45 - Quiet farts).

The Gratitude List

This book also lists interesting trivia or info at the bottom of each page of reasons that correspond to the last one on that page. An added fun feature near the end of the 777 Reasons is a list of 10 reasons for a dog and a cat to be grateful. I think pet owners will appreciate that. To top it off, I include three blank pages to write other reasons you are grateful.

This is a flexible and easy-to-read book. You can pick it up, read a page or two, and get on with your day with a smile on your face. Take it to the bathroom with you or on a trip. Spend 5 minutes or 25 minutes with it. Write in it. Circle the ones that are meaningful to you. Read a page or two in bed before you turn out the light to help your mind relax or bring back a pleasant memory.

I genuinely hope this book will help develop your own sense and practice of gratitude and that you reap the benefits that go with it. Remember to show gratitude to those in your life that have blessed you.

It's your book. It's your life. Enjoy it :)

Thanks for reading,

Craig Jones

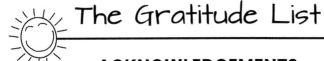

The Gratitude List

ACKNOWLEDGEMENTS

Much thanks to my wife of many years for her valuable input on this book. She has stood by me and supported me through all of my grateful and grumpy times.

Thanks to Stuart Hampton from Pixabay (user:stuarthampton) for the 'Hippie' cover image.

A big thanks to **YOU** for showing an interest in my book.

Thank you!

The Gratitude List

 # 1   Bike rides

 # 2   Teachers that make a difference

 # 3   No unexpected surprises on your DNA test

 # 4   Song lyrics that express what you feel

 # 5   The smell of bacon

 # 6   Funny cat videos

 # 7   Disposable diapers

Marion Donovan invented a waterproof diaper cover which sold at Saks Fifth Avenue in 1949. Two years later she sold her company and the diaper patent for $1,000,000. She had 20 patents in her lifetime.

The Gratitude List

8   Binge-worthy TV marathons

9   Slow-cookers

10   That you learned how to swim

11   Good tires on your vehicle

12   Dog sitters

13   Walking barefoot on the beach

14   Gummy bears

The gummy bear was invented in 1922 by Hans Riegel, Sr. in Germany. He was inspired by the trained dancing bears seen at street festivities in Europe during that time.

The Gratitude List

 # 15   That you weren't in the obituaries today

 # 16   Watching little kids dance

 # 17   Guardian angels

 # 18   Smoothies

 # 19   Catching fireflies (lightning bugs)

 # 20   Being able to make a fresh start

 # 21   Sidewalk chalk

In 2010, the annual Pasadena Chalk Festival was officially named the Largest Display of Chalk Pavement Art by Guinness World Records, and attracted more than 600 artists and 100,000 visitors in one weekend.

The Gratitude List

 # 22   Cats that use their litter box

 # 23   Finding faces in the clouds

 # 24   Comfortable socks

 # 25   When you find something you thought you had lost

 # 26   A glass of wine

 # 27   The sound of wind blowing through the trees

 # 28   A good vacuum cleaner

The Hoover Company marketed a unique vacuum cleaner in the 1960s, called the Constellation. The cylinder type lacked wheels, and instead, floated on its exhaust, operating as a hovercraft.

The Gratitude List

29   Halloween candy

30   A laughing baby

31   A reason to dance

32   Hearing one of your favorite songs

33   Rice cookers

34   That you like who you are

35   T-shirts

In 1904, the Cooper Underwear Company ran a magazine ad for their new 'bachelor undershirt'. It was aimed at men with no wives and no sewing skills.

The Gratitude List

 # 36   Bacon – anytime

 # 37   Flea markets

 # 38   Unexpected gifts

 # 39   That you took that typing class so many years ago

 # 40   People with a sense of humor

 # 41   Unconditional love

 # 42   Rain on a sunny day

Sunny day rain is called a 'sun shower' in the US. In Korea, one term for it is 'fox rain', referring to a legend about a tiger marrying a fox, causing a cloud, who loved the fox, to weep behind the sun.

The Gratitude List

 # 43   Kittens

 # 44   Fall leaves changing colors

 # 45   Quiet farts

 # 46   Having plenty of express lines at the store

 # 47   Dishwashers

 # 48   Peaceful dreams

 # 49   Salt (simple, yet what a difference it makes)

The voyages of Christopher Columbus are said to have been financed from salt production in southern Spain, and the oppressive salt tax in France was one of the causes of the French Revolution.

The Gratitude List

 # 50   Old photographs

 # 51   Beautiful art

 # 52   Homemade chili on a cold day

 # 53   The sound of water in a stream

 # 54   Being cute (you know who you are)

 # 55   A big gas tank in your vehicle

 # 56   Ceiling fans

Rotary ceiling fans in the 1860's were powered by a stream of running water in conjunction with a turbine to drive a system of belts that turned the two-blade fan units.

The Gratitude List

57   Working from home

58   Plenty of closet space

59   Firm handshakes

60   Finding that treasure that was someone's trash

61   Horses

62   Making silly faces

63   When a fortune cookie says just the right thing

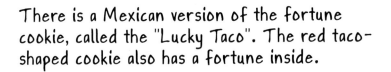

There is a Mexican version of the fortune cookie, called the "Lucky Taco". The red taco-shaped cookie also has a fortune inside.

The Gratitude List

 # 64   Spreadsheet software

 # 65   Athletic shoes

 # 66   When people don't try to talk to you from a different room

 # 67   Museums

 # 68   A bathing suit that makes you look good

 # 69   Microchips for animals

 # 70   A grilled cheese sandwich

The Guinness World Record for the most expensive, commercially available sandwich is the $214 "Quintessential Grilled Cheese", by Serendipity 3 in New York. It even has edible gold flakes!

The Gratitude List

 # 71   Shade trees

 # 72   Finding unexpected money

 # 73   A greeting card that really says how you feel

 # 74   No dog-poop in your yard

 # 75   People that put down their phone and talk with you

 # 76   Banana pudding

 # 77   Polyester

Textile researchers at North Carolina State University are developing a form of polyester that may be as strong as Kevlar, which is used to make bulletproof vests.

The Gratitude List

 # 78   Roses

 # 79   A good listener

 # 80   The moment when your food comes at a restaurant

 # 81   A good stretch when you get up in the morning

 # 82   A good dentist

 # 83   Comfortable underwear

 # 84   Seeing your genealogy

The Family History Library (FamilySearch.org), is the largest genealogical library in the world. It is a free resource that you can use to trace your ancestry.

The Gratitude List

 # 85   Growing your own food

 # 86   The smell of coffee brewing

 # 87   Scary movies

 # 88   Friendly dogs

 # 89   Makeup

 # 90   Non-stick skillets

 # 91   Zippers that always work

In the 1920's, the president of B.F. Goodrich requested some 'slide fasteners' for its company galoshes. He coined the term 'zipper' for the boots and not for the device that fastened them.

The Gratitude List

 # 92   That 'eureka' moment when you solve a problem

 # 93   Seeing a peacock spread its feathers

 # 94   Good water pressure in your home

 # 95   Friendly cashiers

 # 96   Sunglasses

 # 97   A good fishing spot

 # 98   Bananas that are just right to eat

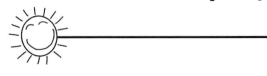

A resident of Jamaica will sometimes have a whole stalk of green bananas in their home. Boiled green bananas and similar dishes are popular there.

99   Wi-Fi (Wireless Networks)

100   Wraparound Porches

101   Christmas movie marathons

102   Reminiscing good times

103   Scenic drives

104   Having a good guitar to play

105   All-You-Can-Eat buffets

The all-you-can-eat style of restaurant was introduced in Las Vegas by Herbert "Herb" Cobb McDonald in 1946. You could eat all you wanted for $1.

The Gratitude List

106   Dog kisses

107   People that know when to keep their mouth shut

108   Natural light in your home

109   Imagination

110   Winning at solitaire

111   Eating Dessert First

112   Free Over-the-Air TV

There are free OTA (over-the-air) channels available today in many areas that are used by 'cord-cutters' with a simple antenna. Many are available in HD and OTA 4K is coming as well.

The Gratitude List

 # 113   Helpful volunteers

 # 114   When you don't lose any socks in the dryer

 # 115   Seeing flocks of migrating birds

 # 116   The ability to let go and move on

 # 117   Looking through your high school yearbook

 # 118   Good conversations

 # 119   Cotton candy

Cotton candy was invented by a dentist and a candy maker in 1897. Originally called "Fairy Floss", they sold 68,655 boxes of it at the 1904 World's Fair.

The Gratitude List

120   Creative people

121   Long weekends

122   The ability to read and write

123   Hoodies

124   Playing in a creek when you were a kid

125   The smell of homemade bread

126   Bird sounds

The brown thrasher has the largest song repertoire of birds, having over 1,000 song types.

The Gratitude List

127   Family reunions

128   Hearing how different people laugh

129   Being debt free (or almost)

130   A tree farm

131   Peace of mind

132   Remembering that first kiss

133   Animal crackers

In 1902, animal crackers became known as "Barnum's Animals" with the familiar circus theme of the Barnum and Bailey Circus. Later in 1902, the box was designed for the Christmas season with the idea of attaching a string to hang from the Christmas tree.

The Gratitude List

 # 134   Movies that makes you laugh

 # 135   Teddy bears

 # 136   Your favorite hot sauce

 # 137   Family — near and far

 # 138   Wrinkle-free clothes

 # 139   Dog parks

 # 140   Knowing how to juggle (or at least trying)

The most soccer balls juggled simultaneously is five.

141   24-Hour Restaurants

142   Honey bees

143   Warm sweaters

144   Good grades

145   Taking a walk

146   Having extra money in the bank

147   Hearing a good Tarzan yell

Johnny Weissmuller, who played Tarzan in the 1930s and 1940s, is best known for the 'Tarzan yell'. The sound itself is a registered trademark and service mark, owned by Edgar Rice Burroughs, Inc., the company that was founded by the author of the Tarzan books.

The Gratitude List

 # 148 A cake that doesn't stick to the pan

 # 149 Thermal underwear

 # 150 Family dinners

 # 151 A well-behaved dog

 # 152 A good book to read

 # 153 The song 'Amazing Grace'

 # 154 A computer mouse

One of the experimental pointing devices developed for a 1960's computer was a head-mounted device attached to the chin or nose. Fortunately, the mouse won out.

The Gratitude List

155 Christmas holidays

156 A big shower with plenty of room

157 Babies – they're all cute

158 Horseback riding

159 A new pair of shoes

160 Working from home

161 A peanut butter and banana sandwich

Sometimes called "The Elvis" as it was a favorite of the King of Rock and Roll, he sometimes had it with bacon on it.

The Gratitude List

 # 162 A smooth writing pen

 # 163 That you aren't on anyone's hit list (you don't think)

 # 164 Hot chocolate with baby marshmallows

 # 165 Being the only person on the beach

 # 166 Bubble baths

 # 167 A good dental hygienist

 # 168 Amusement parks

The first permanent 'Amusement park' was founded in 1895 as Sea Lion Park at Coney Island in NY. It was one of the first to charge admission to get into the park in addition to selling tickets for rides within the park.

The Gratitude List

 # 169   New Year's Day football games

 # 170   A clean house

 # 171   Finding seashells

 # 172   A good podcast

 # 173   Affection

 # 174   Azalea bushes

 # 175   Neckties

In the late 1990's, two researches used mathematical modeling to discover that 85 knots are possible with a conventional tie.

The Gratitude List

176 Good audio speakers

177 A dependable car or truck

178 A good boss

179 Acting like a kid sometimes

180 Thankfulness

181 String quartets

182 Banana splits

The 'Spatula Soda Water Guide' published in 1919 had recipes for 25 banana split varieties.

The Gratitude List

183   Building a snowman

184   A riding lawnmower

185   Achieving goals

186   A good winter coat

187   An encouraging word

188   A clutter-free home

189   Black pepper

Peppercorns are among the most widely traded spice in the world and Vietnam is the world's largest producer and exporter of black peppercorns, yet they use almost none of its production domestically

35

The Gratitude List

190   Sleeping in

191   Free shipping for online shopping

192   Mercy

193   A warm cup of tea

194   A good flashlight

195   Outdoor Christmas lights

196   Doing the hokey pokey

The Hokey Pokey (Hokey Cokey in the UK) originated in a British folk dance with variants dating back to 1826.

 # 197 Having an enjoyable way to spend your time

 # 198 Blue jeans

 # 199 A pumpkin patch

 # 200 A comfortable bed

 # 201 Catching snow on your tongue

 # 202 A backyard firepit

 # 203 Cheese

There are over 1,800 types of cheeses listed at Cheese.com. Cheese is made from milk, not only from cows, but buffalo, camels, goats, reindeer, sheep, and yaks.

The Gratitude List

 # 204 A salad spinner

 # 205 A comfortable chair

 # 206 Popcorn

 # 207 Babysitters

 # 208 Air shows

 # 209 A big computer monitor (or better yet, dual monitors)

 # 210 Clothes hangers

In 1995, while performing surgery in an airliner at 35,000 feet, two doctors used an unfolded coat hanger, sterilized with brandy, as a trocar to stiffen a catheter for use as a chest tube to relieve a passenger's pneumothorax.

The Gratitude List

 # 211 Christmas morning

 # 212 Calm people

 # 213 Being a woman

 # 214 Fairness

 # 215 A good stapler

 # 216 Family vacations

 # 217 Chewing gum

The founder of the chewing gum industry conceived the idea while working for a Mexican leader who chewed a natural gum called chicle. He tried to formulate the gum into a rubber for tires. When that didn't work, he made the chicle into a chewing gum called Chiclets.

 # 218 Ukuleles

 # 219 Clear blue skies

 # 220 Being bare-footed in cool grass on a warm day

 # 221 Blowing bubbles with gum

 # 222 Keeping a journal

 # 223 Chili cheese enchiladas

 # 224 Belly buttons

There are 4 types of 'Outie' belly buttons: Swirly/Spiral, Split, Protrusion, and Circlet. There are 5 types of 'Innie's': Round, Vertical, Oval, T-shaped, and Horizontal.

The Gratitude List

225   Chips and salsa

226   A reason to smile

227   Compassionate people

228   Being single

229   Baby monitors

230   A fire in a fireplace

231   Flying a kite

The World Kite Museum in Long Beach,
Washington has over 1,500 kites from 26
countries around the world.

The Gratitude List

232   Being retired

233   Comfortable shoes

234   Grandchildren

235   Chocolate milk

236   Blanket forts

237   Clear rivers and streams

238   A really good pencil

Thomas Edison had his pencils specially made by Eagle Pencil. Each pencil was three inches long, was thicker than standard pencils and had softer graphite than was normally available.

The Gratitude List

239   Being outdoors

240   Pregnant women and the cute clothes they wear

241   Being unique

242   A good grocery list app

243   Kids car seats

244   Homemade chocolate oatmeal cookies

245   Flip flops

The modern day flip-flop became popular in the US as solders returning from WWII brought the Japanese version called zori, with them.

The Gratitude List

246   Bumper cars

247   A good deck to relax on

248   That final loan payment

249   Clean drinking water

250   Farmers

251   Being able to start over

252   Quirky family holiday traditions

Though Festivus was made famous on Seinfeld, it was conceived by author Daniel O'Keefe and celebrated as early as 1966. If you don't have one, start your own quirky holiday tradition.

The Gratitude List

 # 253 Children drawing pictures

 # 254 Cold watermelon on a hot summer day

 # 255 A good paint job on your house

 # 256 Finding a movie that is good enough to watch more than once

 # 257 A sense of accomplishment

 # 258 Hand-knitted wool socks

 # 259 Chapstick

Chapstick was invented in the 1880's. A commercial artist from Virginia designed the logo for it in 1935 that is still used today. He was paid a one-time fee of $15.

The Gratitude List

260   A good weather app

261   Firefighters

262   Clean breath

263   Listening to grandpa's stories

264   A good pillow

265   Christmas music

266   The smell of rice cooking

For human nutrition, rice is the most important food crop in the world. The world's largest miller and marketer of rice is Riceland Foods in Stuttgart, AR

46

The Gratitude List

267   That you know how to parallel park

268   Going to the zoo

269   Snow ice cream

270   A clean kitchen

271   Cool breezes on a warm day

272   Having a good book to read

273   Baby goats playing

Baby goats have a lot of energy and are fun to watch when they play. If the mood strikes them, they will jump, run, and bounce off objects – sometimes each other.

The Gratitude List

274 Easy to follow travel directions

275 Shadow puppets

276 Rocking chairs

277 Baby kisses

278 That you live where you do

279 Smiles

280 Sunflower seeds

Sunflower seeds with a black husk are usually pressed to extract their oil. Striped sunflower seeds are primarily eaten as a snack food.

The Gratitude List

281 House slippers

282 A cool drink of water

283 Clean jokes

284 A house that feels like home

285 Generous people

286 Children laughing

287 Bubble packing material

The original bubble packing material was invented to be a 3-D wallpaper. That didn't work but it made excellent packing material.

The Gratitude List

288 An unforgettable line from TV

289 Sister time

290 Crab Rangoon

291 A sense of purpose

292 Good neighbors

293 Construction paper

294 Antiperspirant

In the US, the FDA classifies and regulates most deodorants as cosmetics but classifies antiperspirants as over-the-counter drugs.

295   Hand puppets

296   A junk drawer

297   Cooking on an outdoor grill

298   Bird feeders

299   Good role models

300   Being able to have confidence in someone, including yourself

301   Leggings

In the early 1990's, leggings were actually outselling jeans in many parts of the US.

 # 302 After Christmas shopping

 # 303 Ice skating

 # 304 Good windshield wipers

 # 305 Snow cones

 # 306 Doing a belly flop at the swimming pool

 # 307 A quiet house

 # 308 A password manager app

A password manager can save you time and trouble and there are some good ones that are free. Check PCMAG.com for reviews of the best ones.

The Gratitude List

 # 309 Easy to follow assembly instructions

 # 310 A good wife

 # 311 Matching socks

 # 312 Auto correct spelling (most of the time)

 # 313 Country music

 # 314 Fresh air to breath

 # 315 Deviled eggs

Chickens with white ear lobes generally lay white eggs, whereas chickens with red ear lobes lay brown eggs. There is little difference in nutritional value between the two.

The Gratitude List

316 Butterflies

317 Old movies

318 A good thesaurus

319 Cooking marshmallows over a fire

320 A good roommate

321 Marching bands

322 Emery boards

Marie Antoinette was known for her fondness for a nail file-like tool made of pumice stone. The pumice stone was carved into a pencil-like shape, which was used to trim and shape the edges of the nail.

The Gratitude List

 # 323 Having a roof over your head

 # 324 Watching or hearing children play

 # 325 A coffee carafe that doesn't drip when you pour

 # 326 Good BBQ

 # 327 A shopping basket to carry around when you only need a few items at the store

 # 328 Chocolate covered cherries

 # 329 Jigsaw puzzles

Though jigsaw puzzles were originally made from wood, a jigsaw was never actually used to cut it.

The Gratitude List

 # 330   Dried pineapple slices

 # 331   People that are graceful

 # 332   Clean teeth

 # 333   Spending time at grandma's house

 # 334   A soft bed

 # 335   Making snow angels

 # 336   Giving a peanut to an elephant

The elephant's trunk can lift up to 770 pounds, hold over 2 gallons of water, and crack a peanut shell without breaking the seed.

The Gratitude List

337   Crossword puzzles

338   Facial tissue

339   Cream for your coffee

340   Fireworks

341   Christmas stockings

342   A quick charger for your cell phone

343   Rain boots

Rain boots, originally called Wellington boots in honor of the 19th century Duke of Wellington, have a competitive sport named after them called 'Welly Wanging', in which contestants throw a Wellington boot as far as they can. The current world record is about 210 feet.

The Gratitude List

 # 344 Friday nights

 # 345 Happy faces

 # 346 Feeling younger than you are

 # 347 A letter from a friend

 # 348 Antique stores

 # 349 Auto-save software

 # 350 Eating chocolate

Though much of the chocolate consumed today is solid, the ancient Maya drank it. They mixed the paste from the ground cacao seeds with water, chili peppers, and other ingredients. If they sweetened it, they would use honey or flower nectar.

The Gratitude List

351   Parades

352   Lunch with friends

353   A warm blanket

354   The National Anthem

355   Drive-through restaurants

356   A warm scarf

357   Paper clips

Though there were more than 50 paper clip patents prior to 1900, the most common paper clip still in use today is the "Gem paper clip", which was never patented. National Paper Clip Day is May 29th.

The Gratitude List

358   A wood stove

359   Clean diapers

360   Green traffic lights

361   Family recipes handed down

362   Access to a local health or fitness club

363   Good weather

364   Hearing a cat purr

Cats purr for different reasons and the purring can have a different sound. Sometimes they want to be fed and other times they are just happy

The Gratitude List

 # 365 Hearing someone's story

 # 366 Happy memories

 # 367 Farmer's markets

 # 368 Bluetooth speakers

 # 369 Stretch pants

 # 370 Food Trucks

 # 371 Holding hands

Holding hands has many health benefits. It can lower blood pressure and heart rate and put you in a more relaxed state.

The Gratitude List

372   Forbearance

373   Earplugs to drown out snoring and other noises

374   Air conditioning

375   A good blender

376   Honest people

377   Being appreciated at work

378   Barcodes

The barcode was patented in the US in 1951 and was based on Morse code. They became commercially successful when they were used to automate supermarket checkout systems in the 1970's.

The Gratitude List

379 Kayaking

380 Homemade gifts

381 Streaming movies

382 Making new friends

383 Ocean sounds and smells

384 Hammocks

385 Fresh baked chocolate chip cookies

The chocolate chip cookie was invented by Ruth Graves Wakefield and Sue Brides in 1938 when Wakefield owned Toll House Inn in Massachusetts. The original recipe is available online.

The Gratitude List

386   Fresh batteries

387   Acceptance

388   Sundresses

389   Fried chicken

390   A good family doctor

391   Air fresheners

392   Hummingbirds

During hovering and flight, the heart rate of a hummingbird can reach 1,260 beats per minute.

The Gratitude List

 # 393   Fresh fruit

 # 394   Beautiful clouds

 # 395   Interesting people

 # 396   Caller ID

 # 397   Black Friday sales

 # 398   A fitting quotation

 # 399   A good sewing machine

I know someone that still uses a solidly built Kenmore machine they bought new in 1971.

The Gratitude List

400   Sweatpants

401   Dessert

402   Having a winning lottery ticket of any amount

403   Aroma therapy candles

404   Going on a cruise

405   Growing up in a small town

406   Crayons

Early French artist Francois Clouet (1510–1572) used crayons for his elaborate modeled portraits. They so impressed Henry V, that he was knighted and became a court painter for the royalty

66

The Gratitude List

407   Juke boxes

408   Fresh seafood

409   Mosquito nets

410   People that help you work through your mistakes instead of criticizing you

411   Fresh ideas

412   Forgiveness

413   Jar openers

The jar opener is a type of 'Gilhoolie', which was invented in 1952 by Dr. C.W. Fuller, a retired dentist. Although Fuller held more than a dozen patents in the fields of dentistry and golf, the Gilhoolie patent was his only patent for a kitchen device.

The Gratitude List

414   Puppy videos

415   Watching a favorite TV show

416   Fresh cinnamon rolls

417   Meeting up with old friends

418   A good nights sleep

419   A big pile of leaves to jump in as a kid

420   Cloud storage

Cloud storage is a fantastic way to save your photos and important documents online and you will have them even if your computer crashes or is stolen. It's a low-cost or free solution that could save you a big headache.

The Gratitude List

421 Line dancing

422 When things are going your way

423 Decorating the Christmas tree

424 Candles for when the lights go out

425 A good rewarding job

426 Fried okra

427 Clowns at the circus

The antics of circus clowns are fun to watch for most people but almost 8% of Americans have coulrophobia, the fear of clowns.

The Gratitude List

428   Faith

429   A kitchen pantry

430   Photosynthesis

431   National parks

432   Masking tape

433   Seeing an eagle

434   Electric blankets

A cartoon electrical blanket named "Blanky", was portrayed in the 1987 film 'The Brave Little Toaster'.

The Gratitude List

 # 435   Frozen vegetables

 # 436   Hearing a funny story

 # 437   A good workout

 # 438   Carpeting

 # 439   Having an avenue to express yourself

 # 440   Having opposable thumbs

 # 441   Digital photos

With digital photos you can take as many as you want – keep the good ones and delete the rest. Save them online and you will always have them. And they won't deteriorate. Not like the old days of film photos.

The Gratitude List

 # 442 A cab driver who doesn't talk to you

 # 443 Good hair days

 # 444 Coupons

 # 445 Selfies

 # 446 Freedom of religion

 # 447 Trying new restaurants

 # 448 Looking through a kaleidoscope

The word "kaleidoscope", was derived from 3 Ancient Greek words to mean "observation of beautiful forms". Its patent was granted to Scotsman David Brewster in 1817.

The Gratitude List

449 Gluten-free food

450 Clean sheets

451 Funny nicknames

452 That someone loves you

453 Nurses

454 Camping

455 Email

Computer programmer Ray Tomlinson invented email in 1971 and he is the one that chose the @ symbol to separate the user name from their machine (domain).

The Gratitude List

456   Paint by numbers

457   Hugs

458   Grocery stores

459   Adhesive bandages

460   When someone else loads or unloads the dishwasher

461   Parks with a playground for kids

462   Compliments

A sincere compliment benefits both the giver and receiver. It doesn't cost anything to give one to someone else. Mark Twain said "I can live for two months on a good compliment."

The Gratitude List

 # 463   Hair spray

 # 464   Being in love

 # 465   Good ear buds

 # 466   The memories you get when looking at your passport stamps

 # 467   A good pot of soup

 # 468   Hearing scary stories at night

 # 469   Iron skillets

Cast-iron pots and pans from the 19th and 20th century continue to see daily use to the present day. They are also highly sought after by antique collectors and dealers.

The Gratitude List

470   Pajamas with feet

471   God's grace

472   Cookbooks

473   That you have weird friends (but you aren't weird)

474   Dryer balls

475   Leak-proof sippy cups

476   GPS

GPS enabled smartphones are typically accurate to within a 16 feet radius under open sky. It gets worse near buildings, bridges, and trees.
Source: GPS.gov

The Gratitude List

477 Freedom of speech

478 The sound of owls hooting

479 Healthy foods

480 Fun emojis

481 Electricity

482 Flowers blooming in the spring

483 ATM's

ATM PINs were originally intended to have 6 digits. When the inventor tested the system on his wife, she could only remember 4 digits so that became the world standard.

The Gratitude List

484 Sending or receiving Christmas cards

485 A good set of dishes

486 Seeing a shooting star

487 Toothpaste

488 Open minded people

489 Living in a free country

490 Warm doughnuts

National Doughnut Day is celebrated in the US on the first Friday of June of each year, succeeding the Doughnut event created by The Salvation Army in Chicago in 1938 to honor their members who served doughnuts to soldiers during World War I.

The Gratitude List

491   Dollar Stores

492   Advances in modern medicine

493   Music that moves you

494   Programmable coffee makers

495   Easter egg hunts

496   Finding treasures in the attic

497   Dental floss

Even monkeys floss their teeth. A Japanese macaque has been observed in the wild and in captivity flossing with human hair and feathers.

The Gratitude List

498   Seeing snow fall

499   Excellence

500   Home cooked meals

501   Being addiction-free

502   Peaceful days

503   Garbage disposals

504   Good free apps for your computer, tablet, or phone

There are so many great free apps/software available. A great source to find the best ones is at PCMAG.com

The Gratitude List

 # 505 Watching crabs play in the sand

 # 506 Organized people

 # 507 Joy

 # 508 The absence of political talk

 # 509 Computers that work right

 # 510 Butterfly kisses

 # 511 Duct tape

The wide-scale adoption of duct tape, came from a factory worker and mother of two Navy sailors, who worried that problems with ammunition box seals would cost soldiers precious time in battle. She wrote to FDR about it and the rest is history.

The Gratitude List

512   Mouse traps

513   True friends

514   The view of snow covered mountains

515   Air travel

516   Emotional strength

517   March Madness

518   Houseplants

Various houseplants can put more oxygen in the air, provide allergy relief, and help you to focus better. Source: WebMD.com

The Gratitude List

519 Watching your dog dream

520 Picnics on a sunny day

521 Neon lights

522 Being cancer-free

523 Garbage pick-up in your neighborhood

524 People that are genuine

525 Jelly beans

When Beatlemania broke out in 1963, fans of the Beatles in the US pelted the band with jelly beans (emulating fans in the UK who threw the British candy Jelly Babies at George Harrison, who reportedly liked eating them).

The Gratitude List

526   Learning new things

527   Fresh cut flowers

528   Finding a bargain

529   Independence

530   Sailing

531   Hot apple cider

532   Remote controls

The first TV remote came out in 1950,
dubbed "Lazy Bones", was linked to the TV set
by a long wire. In 1956 a wireless remote was
developed called "Zenith Space Command".

 # 533 Drinking milk straight from a coconut

 # 534 People that do their jobs properly

 # 535 Date nights

 # 536 Elevators

 # 537 Hot apple pie with vanilla ice cream

 # 538 Being well-rested

 # 539 Microwave ovens

The heating effect of a microwave beam was discovered by Percy Spencer accidently in 1945 when it started to melt a chocolate bar in his pocket as he was working on radar equipment.

The Gratitude List

 # 540   Learning toys

 # 541   A good haircut

 # 542   When your dog is happy to see you

 # 543   Hot buttered rolls

 # 544   Happy memories of loved ones who have passed

 # 545   People and media that use correct grammar

 # 546   Flower gardens

The 'Dallas Blooms' festival lasts for 6 weeks. It has 70 acres of gardens with half a million tulips, 7,500 violas and about 15,000 pansies, among others. There are many other activities in addition to viewing the flowers.

547   Snow days at school when you were a kid

548   Road trips

549   People that are not always on their phone

550   Teamwork

551   Justice

552   A good side hustle

553   Peanut butter

The United States is a leading exporter of peanut butter, and itself consumes $800 million of peanut butter annually.

The Gratitude List

554 Home ownership

555 Playing outside as a kid

556 Quiet mornings

557 Seeing new life

558 Seeing the stars at night

559 People that are on time

560 Smart phones

According to the U.N., more people on earth have access to cell phones than toilets

The Gratitude List

561   Getting a massage

562   Technology that makes life better

563   Sledding in the snow

564   Homemade cheesecake

565   Bifocals

566   Holiday candles

567   Laughing so much it makes me snort

Laughter has been used as a therapeutic tool for many years because it is a natural form of medicine – it provides benefits to a person's physical, emotional, and social well being.

The Gratitude List

568 Payday

569 Scenic old bridges

570 Handwritten letters

571 Uninterrupted dinners

572 Noise canceling headphones

573 Good co-workers

574 Scotch tape

Early versions of Scotch tape were known as cellophane tape. Scotty McTape, a kilt-wearing cartoon boy, was the brand's mascot for two decades, first appearing in 1944. The familiar tartan design, a take on the well-known Wallace tartan, was introduced in 1945.

The Gratitude List

 # 575 Clocks that reset themselves for Daylight Saving Time

 # 576 Mason jars

 # 577 Having a 401K plan to help in retirement

 # 578 Playing board games

 # 579 Indoor plumbing

 # 580 Seeing joy on a child's face

 # 581 Peppermint sticks

Stick candy has been around since the 1830's. It was the subject of an 1885 song "The Candy Stick", a 1907 poem "Stick-Candy Days" and a 1909 poem, "The Land of Candy".

The Gratitude List

582 Rock 'n' roll music

583 Getting a good report from a blood test

584 That you aren't in school any more

585 Iced coffee

586 People that make you laugh

587 Nail salons

588 The sound of croaking frogs

A frog's tongue can snatch prey 5 times faster than you can blink. Though the tongue is covered with a saliva like substance, the saliva becomes thicker than honey outside the mouth, sticking to its prey as it pulls it into its mouth.

The Gratitude List

589 Slow dancing with that special person

590 Instant oatmeal

591 LED lights

592 Polite drivers on the road

593 That you have a sense of humor

594 The words "I love you"

595 Orchids

One of the most beautiful flowers in the world,
some varieties have a use as a food source.
The dried seed pods of orchid genus Vanilla, is
commercially important as a flavoring in baking,
for perfume manufacture and aromatherapy.

The Gratitude List

596   Patience

597   Saturday mornings

598   Prayer

599   The circus

600   Completing a difficult task

601   Playing video games

602   Homemade chicken noodle soup

Chicken soup has long been a form of folk medicine to treat symptoms of the common cold. It does contain an amino acid that is very similar to acetylcysteine, which is used by doctors for patients with bronchitis and other respiratory infections to help clear them.

94

The Gratitude List

603   Living in a small town

604   Permanent markers

605   Clothes dryers

606   Ice cubes

607   Sweater weather

608   Good eyesight

609   Roller coasters

The world's tallest roller coaster, the Kingda Ka in NJ, reaches a height of 456 feet before dropping 418 feet. It reaches its top speed of 128 mph in 3.5 seconds.

The Gratitude List

#610   People that show respect

#611   Traveling to new places

#612   Poetry

#613   Campfires

#614   Libraries

#615   Helping others

#616   Sliced bread

Sliced bread was first sold in 1928. In 1943, the US imposed a short-lived ban against it as a wartime conservation measure. With much public outcry, the ban was rescinded after only 7 weeks.

The Gratitude List

617   The Aurora Borealis

618   Flannel sheets on cool nights

619   Thanksgiving dinner

620   People with common sense

621   Hearing good news

622   Sunscreen

623   Paper towels

Americans are the highest users of paper towels in the home, compared to the people in any other country. People in the Middle East tend to prefer reusable cloth towels, and people in Europe tend to prefer reusable cleaning sponges.

The Gratitude List

624   Good hearing

625   Free Samples

626   People that you feel comfortable with

627   Mashed potatoes and gravy

628   Time to yourself

629   The smell of fresh-cut grass

630   Glitter

Today over 20,000 varieties of glitter are manufactured in a vast number of different colors, sizes, and materials.

The Gratitude List

 # 631   A lack of complications

 # 632   Blowing bubbles made from soapy water

 # 633   People that are dreamers

 # 634   Something to look forward to

 # 635   The desert at night

 # 636   Homemade ice cream when you were a kid

 # 637   The sound of katydids in the evening

The sound of some katydids depends on the temperature, and you can get a fairly accurate reading this way. Generally the number of chirps in 15 seconds, plus 37 is the temperature in Fahrenheit.

The Gratitude List

 # 638   Matches for lighting candles

 # 639   Getting a manicure

 # 640   When you cook over easy eggs that look good

 # 641   Having good health

 # 642   Porch swings

 # 643   Jesus

 # 644   Cherry blossom trees

In 1912, Japan gave 3,000 cherry trees to the city of Washington, DC to celebrate the friendship between the US and Japan. The National Cherry Blossom Festival occurs every spring in our nation's capital.

The Gratitude List

645   Pastries – any kind

646   Tire swings

647   Love letters

648   Stained glass windows

649   Holiday parties

650   Random acts of kindness

651   Zip lining

The oldest person to ride a zip-line is Jack
Reynolds of the UK. He did it on his 106th
birthday in 2018.

The Gratitude List

 # 652   When things work out in the end

 # 653   Roasted peanuts

 # 654   Privacy fences

 # 655   Health insurance

 # 656   The freedom to vote

 # 657   Treehouses

 # 658   Piñatas

The Pinata is of Chinese origin. It was in the shape of a cow or ox and was decorated with symbols and colors meant to produce a favorable climate for the coming growing season. It was filled with five types of seeds and then hit with sticks of various colors.

The Gratitude List

 # 659 Playing golf

 # 660 A good hot shower

 # 661 Patriotism

 # 662 A scenic train ride

 # 663 Salt and vinegar potato chips

 # 664 Streaming music

 # 665 Toilet paper

Toilet paper in colors such as pink, lavender, light blue, light green, purple, green, and light yellow was commonly sold in the US from the 1960s but gradually went out of favor and is now only sold as a novelty item.

The Gratitude List

666   Software that works right

667   Kisses

668   A garden hose

669   S'mores

670   Robotic vacuum cleaners

671   Self-reliant people

672   Blow dryers (hair dryer)

The first hairdryer was invented in 1890. It was a large, seated version that consisted of a bonnet that attached to the chimney pipe of a gas stove. The handheld hair dryer first appeared in 1920.

The Gratitude List

 # 673 Hot pizza

 # 674 Handheld back scratchers

 # 675 Battery powered leaf blowers

 # 676 Tablet computers

 # 677 Untouched snow on the ground

 # 678 Watching and playing in the tide on the beach

 # 679 Webcams

The first webcam, developed in 1991, was used to monitor a coffee pot at the Cambridge University Computer Science Department.

The Gratitude List

680   Heated car seats

681   Commercial-free TV

682   A good church

683   Teeth whiteners

684   Hiking

685   The smell of a live Christmas tree

686   Toilets that always flush properly

Crapper' was a coarse name for a toilet that gained popularity from the work of Thomas Crapper, who popularized flush toilets in England. He had 3 patents for toilet related improvements.

The Gratitude List

687 When your investments do well

688 The sound of a gentle rain

689 Police officers

690 Bowling

691 Homemade quilts

692 Watching a child learn to tie their shoes

693 Morning coffee – there's nothing like it

The 'coffee break' originated in the late 19th century in Stoughton, Wisconsin with the wives of Norwegian immigrants. The city celebrates this every year with the Stoughton Coffee Break Festival.

The Gratitude List

694   Audio books

695   Gift cards

696   The beautiful colors in the sunset

697   Beards

698   Sincere apologies

699   The smell of a roast cooking

700   White sand beaches

50 billion tons of beach sand and fossil sand is used each year for construction. Desert sand, although plentiful, is not suitable for construction because of its composition.

The Gratitude List

 # 701 The holiday spirit

 # 702 Good in-laws

 # 703 Digital Cameras

 # 704 Weekends

 # 705 Parking spaces near the front

 # 706 Warm sun on a cool day

 # 707 Sticky notes

The yellow color of the original sticky notes was chosen by accident, as the lab where they were developed only had yellow scrap paper to use.

708   A glass of really cold milk

709   Kids birthday parties

710   Beautiful singing

711   Fantasy football

712   People that listen more than they speak

713   Washing machines

714   The smell of patchouli oil

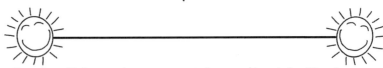

Patchouli is an important ingredient in East Asian incense. Both patchouli oil and incense increased in popularity in the 1960s and 1970s, mainly as a result of the hippie movement. Indonesia produces over 90% of the world's Patchouli oil.

The Gratitude List

 # 715 Siding for your house

 # 716 Living pain-free (most of the time)

 # 717 Kind words

 # 718 Living close to work

 # 719 That you are a list maker

 # 720 Sleepovers when you were a kid

 # 721 Hot dogs

The wife of a German immigrant who sold 'frankfurters' in St. Louis, came up with the idea of putting them in a bun. Previously they were 'bun-less' and customers were given gloves to handle the 'hot' dogs.

The Gratitude List

\# 722   Ice cream toppings

\# 723   People watching from a park bench

\# 724   A good husband

\# 725   Watching a sunrise

\# 726   Plenty of cabinet space in the kitchen

\# 727   The simple things in life

\# 728   Bird watching

A 'bird-watcher' is typically a person with a casual interest in the activity. A 'birder' is one who seriously pursues the hobby of 'birding'. There are about 10,000 bird species in the world and only a few people have seen more than 7,000.

The Gratitude List

 # 729 Sweet tea

 # 730 Music boxes

 # 731 Good sheets

 # 732 Never having a broken bone

 # 733 A toolbox with quality tools

 # 734 People that can see the good in any person

 # 735 Traffic roundabouts

Modern roundabouts were first standardized in the UK in 1966. The first one built in the U.S. was in Nevada in 1990. They are generally met with resistance prior to construction but are favored when drivers gain experience with them.

The Gratitude List

736 Harp music

737 The Macy's Thanksgiving Day parade

738 Online shopping

739 Inspiration

740 High school class reunions

741 The Internet

742 Roller skating

The first patented roller skate was by a Belgian inventor in 1760 wasn't much more than an ice skate with wheels where the blade goes, a style we would call inline today. They were hard to steer and hard to stop, thus were not very popular.

The Gratitude List

743   A good nap

744   A perfectly cooked steak

745   A good playlist

746   Watching the ocean

747   Military veterans

748   Soaking tubs

749   Forever stamps

The United States Postal Service unveiled the 'Forever' stamp in 2007 at an original price of 41 cents. The Forever stamp is always valid for the full first-class postage regardless of any rate increases since the stamp was purchased.

The Gratitude List

750   Touring a castle

751   Singing along with a song that you know

752   Vaccines

753   The smell of rosemary

754   Smoke detectors

755   Knowing what you are good at

756   The beauty of the moon

There is a phenomenon called a 'moonbow' similar to a sunlight rainbow. They are very faint and usually appear to the eyes to be white. However, the colors of the moonbow can be seen in long exposure photographs.

The Gratitude List

757 The sound of wind chimes

758 Walk-in closets

759 Sunny winter days

760 Whipped cream

761 Optimistic people

762 The feel of a child's hand in mine

763 Nail clippers

Prior to the invention of the modern nail clipper, people would use small knives to trim or pare their nails. Descriptions of nail trimming in literature date as far back as the 8th century BC.

The Gratitude List

764   Pancakes and syrup

765   Objective people

766   Overcoming a fear

767   Phone texting

768   Wisdom

769   Vacation days

770   Ladybugs

Many cultures consider ladybugs lucky and have
nursery rhymes or local names for them that
reflect this. One popular nursery rhyme was
'Ladybird Ladybird'.

The Gratitude List

771   Yard sales

772   Waterfalls

773   Truckers - the backbone of America

774   Good handwriting

775   Watching your cat do silly stuff

776   Trying new recipes

777   Rainbows

A rainbow is not something that can be physically approached. It is an optical illusion caused by any water droplets viewed from a certain angle relative to a light source. Even if you see someone that appears to be at the end of a rainbow, they themselves cannot see that.

The Gratitude List

for DOGS

1   When my person comes home

2   Chasing the cat

3   Treats

4   Drinking from the toilet

5   Having friends to play with

6   Going for walks

7   Meal time

8   A big yard to play in

9   A good bone to chew on

10   When my person tells me I'm good

The Gratitude List

for CATS

1   That I'm not a dog

2   Staring contests with humans

3   Plenty of places to take a nap

4   Toilet paper to play with

5   A good scratching post, like a sofa

6   Having humans available if I need them

7   Plenty of space to run in my house
       when I get the zoomies

8   An empty box or bag

9   Jumping onto the dining table

10   Plenty of windows so I can survey my
       kingdom

The Gratitude List

Other reasons you are Grateful

_____

_____

_____

_____

_____

_____

_____

_____

_____

_____

_____

_____

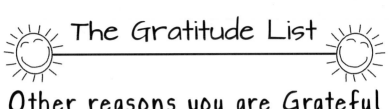

The Gratitude List

Other reasons you are Grateful

_____

_____

_____

_____

_____

_____

_____

_____

_____

_____

_____

_____

_____

The Gratitude List

Other reasons you are Grateful

_____

_____

_____

_____

_____

_____

_____

_____

_____

_____

_____

_____

_____

AUTHOR INFO

Craig Jones is the author
of two children's picture books.

Both are available at Amazon
in paperback, hardback, and Kindle versions.

The hardback version is also available in Ingram's
catalog for libraries and other retail markets.

Slow Down Turtle

A story about a turtle
who did not realize how
special he was.
Rather than embracing
his own uniqueness,
he wanted to be
like his friends.
But through a series
of adventures,
he discovered just how
special he really was.

978-1-7331853-0-1 (PB)

978-1-7331853-1-8 (HB)

**Library of Congress
Control Number:
2019943741**

Silly Rhymes for Boys and Girls

A book of original
'Nonsense Rhymes'
that children will love to
hear and read.
Edward Lear and Lewis
Carroll popularized this
style in the 19th century,
and others have
continued it up to
the present day.
'Silly Rhymes for Boys &
Girls' is sure to get a
giggle out of the young
ones and those that
are young at heart.

978-1-7331853-3-2 (PB)

978-1-7331853-4-9 (HB)

**Library of Congress
Control Number:
2020931686**

Look for an upcoming **Gratitude Journal**
by Craig Jones that can be used
alongside or separate from **'The Gratitude List.'**